Fish Don't Need Snorkels

by
Karen Collum

illustrated by Chiara Vercesi

Does a fish need a snorkel to breathe under water?

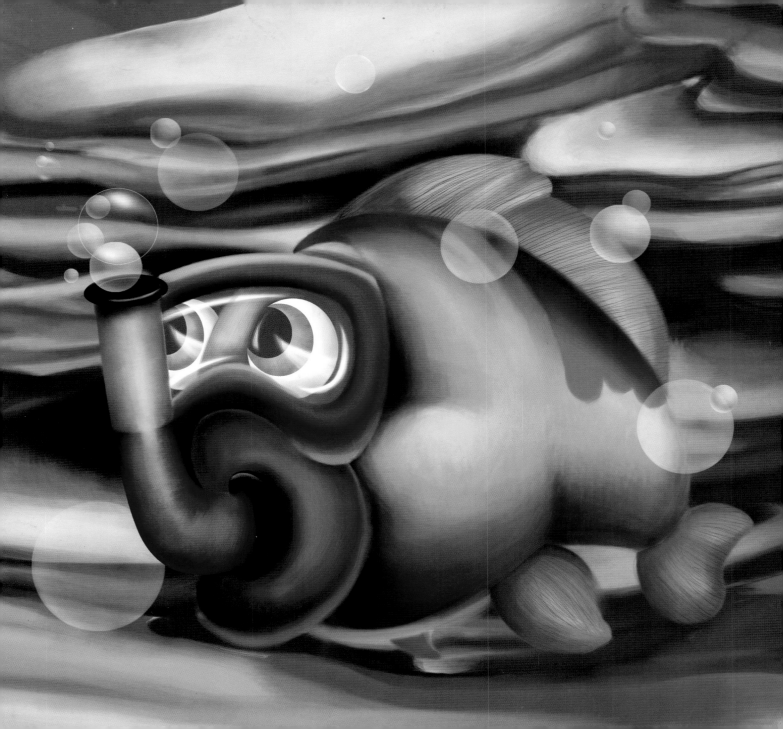

God gave the fish
gills to breathe under water.

Does a giraffe need a ladder to reach the top of the tree?

God gave the giraffe a long neck to reach the top of the tree.

Does a turtle need to search for
a house to live in?

God gave the turtle a shell to live in.

Does a mountain goat need a trampoline to jump over the rocks?

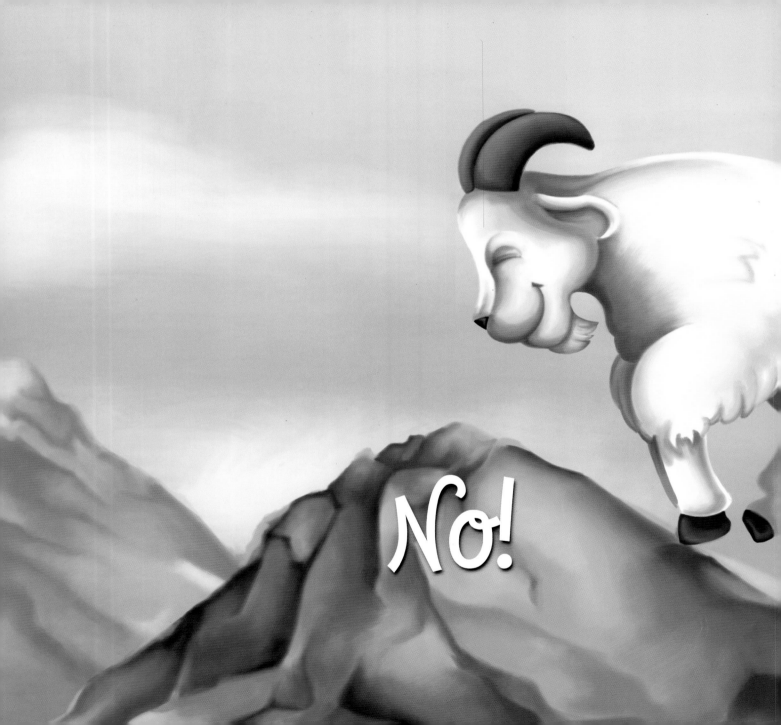

God gave the mountain
goat strong legs to jump
over the rocks.

Does an elephant need a straw to drink from the river?

Does a bird need a
hang-glider to fly across the sky?

No!

God gave the bird wings to fly across the sky.

Do you
have wings

or gills

or a shell

or a trunk?

No!

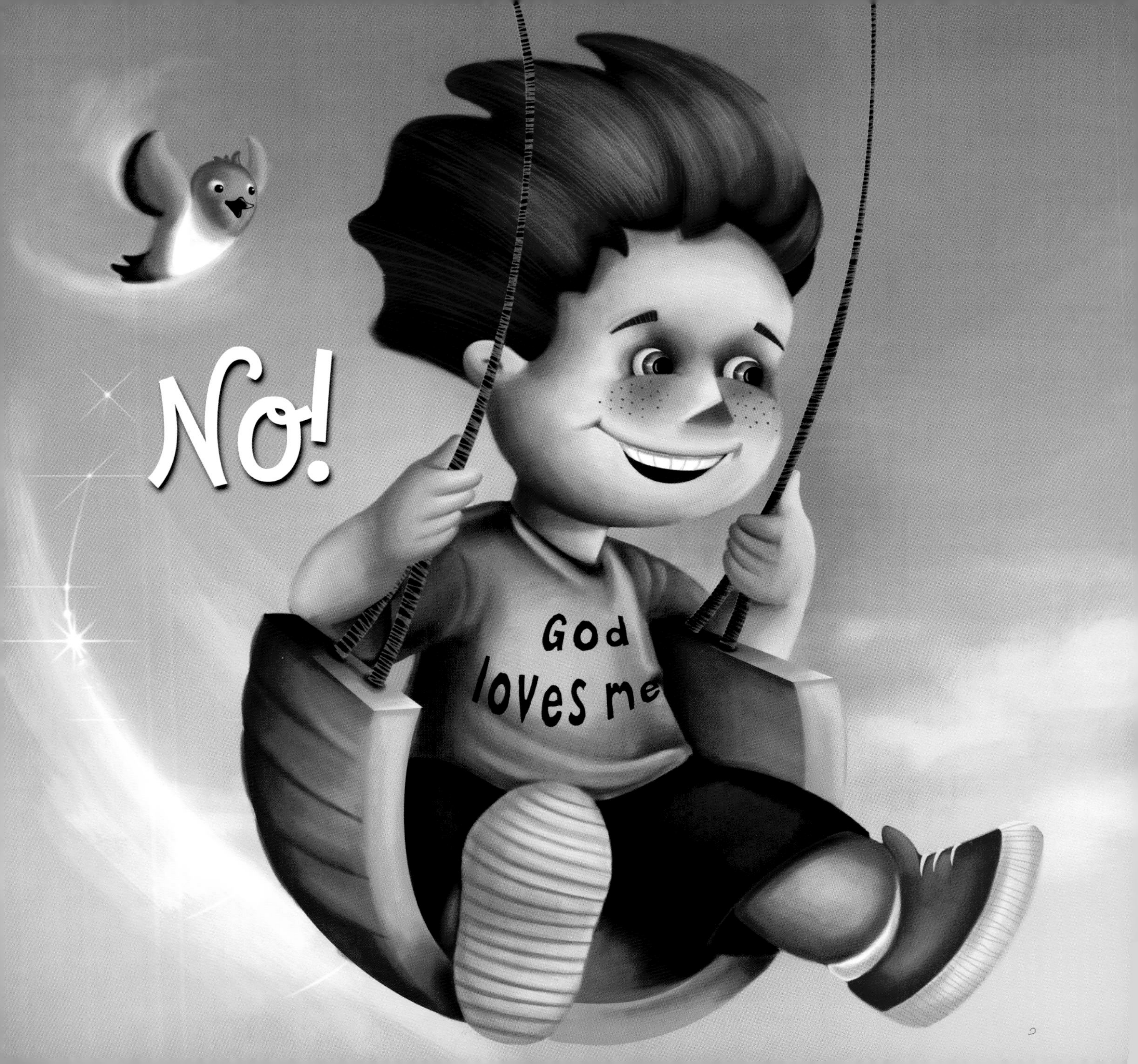

God made you in his image.
And he loves you just
the way you are.

First published in 2010
Copyright © 2010 Autumn House Publishing (Europe) Ltd.

Author: Karen Collum

Illustrator: Chiara Vercesi

British Library Cataloguing in Publication Data.
A catalogue record for this book is available from the British Library.

ISBN 978-1-906381-96-7

Published by Autumn House, Alma Park, Grantham, Lincs.

Printed in China

My Bible counting book

by Anne Pilmoor

illustrated by Chiara Vercesi

Children will enjoy this book as the scene develops
on each double page. The simple text and bright,
colourful illustrations will make this a favourite
counting book for nursery-age children.

Also published by Autumn House

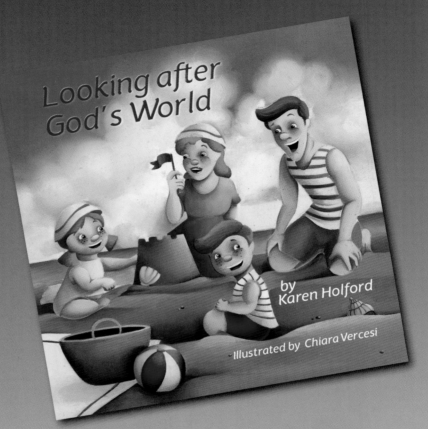

Looking after God's World

by Karen Holford

Illustrated by Chiara Vercesi

What would it feel like to be God and make a whole wonderful world? What would it feel like if your beautiful world was ruined? Tim and Susie wonder about these big questions while they build sandcastles on the beach. Join in their adventures when disaster strikes and they learn how to look after God's wonderful world.

Also published by Autumn House